S0-AGX-088

Space Fruit

by Carol Pugliano-Martin
illustrated by Claire Louise Milne

Table of Contents

Chapter 1

Mica

My name is Mica and I hate apples. I hate any food made with apples. I hate apple pie, applesauce, and just plain apples. There is a reason why I hate apples so much. My family owns an apple farm.

For my family, growing apples is traditional. My mother and sister wear apples on their dresses, and my father and brother wear apple bandannas. Isn't it obvious why I hate apples?

It's not only my family that loves apples. All my friends love apples, too. My friends think I'm lucky to live on an apple farm. Everyone thinks something is wrong with me because I think apples are disgusting.

It's hard working on the farm because I have to be around apples all the time. I have to pick them and polish them, but I definitely won't eat them.

I don't like apples, and I also don't like cows. If you've ever been kicked by a cow, then you'll know why I don't like them. Maybe they are mad because I don't like their milk. Our cows kick so much that sometimes I think they are trying to be funny. I think when they moo they are really just laughing at me.

My life is very complex. I need a strategy to get me out of all this farmwork. I also need to get my mom to stop making every meal with apples. Fried apples with apple butter, apple juice, and ice cream topped with apples! If all that isn't bad enough, I have to write a science report on a planet for homework tonight.

Chapter 2

The Strange Plant

I handed in my science report today. I can't even remember what I wrote! I wrote about Jupiter, but I don't remember anything about the planet.

When I got home from school today, there was chaos at the farm. Everyone was so excited!

"If you didn't plant it, then how did it get here?" my mother yelled.

My father didn't know how it got there, but he said we had to get rid of it. What was my family talking about?

"What's going on?" I asked.

"This!" shouted my mother as she pointed to a strange tree in the middle of the apple orchard.

At first I thought it looked like all the other trees. But then I noticed the extraordinary fruit that was growing on the tree. Each piece of fruit was round, yellow, and had one big red spot on it.

"Mica, get an ax and help me cut this thing down," ordered my father. "I can't have it ruining the crop!"

I started to walk toward the barn, but just then there was a huge bang of thunder. Lightning streaked across the sky.

"Mica, get inside. A big storm's coming!" shouted my mother. We left the odd tree and went inside. During the storm, some of the fruit fell down. It rolled into the barn and the hen house.

Later that night, when the storm was over, my dad and I went outside to chop the tree down. We chopped and chopped, and finally the stubborn tree fell down.

"Hey Dad," I whispered. "Look at that."

"Wow!" said my father. There was a glowing hole in the spot where the tree was cut down.

"It must be from the lightning," said my father. "Now, let's throw out this bizarre fruit. Everything will be back to normal in the morning."

He was wrong.

The next morning, my little sister Sally burst into the kitchen. Everyone was eating apple omelets except for me. I was eating toast.

"Look at the eggs from the henhouse," said Sally.

Each egg in Sally's basket had a big red spot on it! My mom checked the eggshells from the eggs they had eaten for breakfast. They had red spots on them, too. We ran to the henhouse. Every hen had a big red spot on her feathers!

My brother Hank came in and asked what was going on. My father asked if he had just woken up.

"I've been awake long enough to eat some of Mama's delicious omelets," said Hank.

"Oh, sweetheart, maybe you shouldn't have eaten those omelets," said my mother. "We don't know what's happening with these eggs."

We were about to find out.

Clue: Into the kitchen is a prepositional phrase. Can you find a prepositional phrase on this page that describes where Mica's family runs?

Chapter 3

Spots

Suddenly, everyone in my family had a big, red, glowing spot on them! I recognized that glow!

"The tree!" I shouted as we all ran outside.

When we got to the place where the tree had been, we all stopped and stared. There was a huge red spot in the dirt now. There was no shortage of strangeness on our farm! Then we noticed the cows. Our cows now had big glowing red spots on them!

Suddenly, I figured it out! The cows and the hens had eaten the fruit! I told my family my theory.

I pointed to the place where the tree once stood. There was still part of a half-eaten, red-spotted fruit on the ground. My father nodded his head seriously. He looked around at our red-spotted family. Then his eyes landed on me and stayed there.

"Mica, you don't have a red spot. Why?"

He was right. I told him that I was the only one who hadn't eaten the eggs.

"You might be right!" said my father. "The hens ate the fruit, and we ate the hens' eggs. Oh, no, the milk!"

We all ran toward the barn.

My dad spotted Bill, one of the men who worked on our farm, carrying two buckets of milk from our cows.

"Bill, don't sell the milk!" yelled my father.

It was too late. Bill had already sent a huge shipment of our milk out to the stores.

We looked inside the buckets of milk. The creamy white milk had a big red spot on the top! Bill had a white milk moustache above his upper lip. And right in the middle of his nose was a glowing red spot!

The next few days were crazy. The milk had gone to the local stores, and everyone in town had drunk the milk. Suddenly, all over town, people had big, glowing red spots on them.

Clue: Suddenly is an introductory word separated from the rest of the sentence by a comma. Can you find another example on page 8?

One night while my family was watching television, our town's mayor appeared on the screen. He looked very nervous. A big red spot was glowing on his bald head.

"My fellow townspeople, this is extremely urgent," the mayor said. "What's happening to our civilization? This disease has spread throughout our entire town! We have not faced a problem like this since the founding of our town. We must find a solution!"

My family turned to look at me. I realized that I was the only person for miles around that did not have a spot.

Chapter 4

The Discovery

The next day in science class, our teacher, Mrs. Banks, returned our science reports. So much had happened since I had written that report on Jupiter.

Throughout the class, all of my red-spotted classmates turned to look at me. I think they thought if they stared hard enough, a big red spot would appear on me, too. I just stared back.

"Remember, students, all of the answers are found in science," Mrs. Banks said. She really loved science! I had never really cared about science before. But this time, when Mrs. Banks talked about the wonders of science, I listened. Maybe science *was* the answer.

I looked down at my science report. On the front page I had put a picture of Jupiter. Now I was staring at the picture. In the picture, Jupiter was round and yellow, with a big red spot on it! I made an important discovery!

As soon as the bell rang, I raced out of school. I had to get to the library. I burst through the doors of the library and ran to a computer. I typed in the word "Jupiter" to see what I could find. After searching for a while, I found some information.

Jupiter's red spot is really a powerful storm that's always brewing. The red spot on Jupiter looked just like the spots on everyone in town. But what was the connection? I found the answer in a science journal. Once every century, something unusual happens in Jupiter's storm. The strong winds send tiny particles out into space. The particles had landed on our farm and grown into the mystery tree and, well, you know the rest.

I ran out of the library and headed straight for the mayor's office!

Chapter 5

Here Comes the Sun

I couldn't believe I was sitting in the mayor's office telling him about my discovery. The mayor was intrigued. In fact, he thought I had done great scientific work, and that my hypothesis made sense.

"You've figured out the problem, but what's the solution?" asked the mayor.

I breathed a sigh of relief. I had the solution all figured out. I excitedly told the mayor my plan.

The next day was quite an amazing scene.

"Please remember your sunglasses everyone! That goes for animals too!" shouted the mayor into his megaphone.

The town was filled with people lying in the sun, and it was all because of me. I thought that since a sunny day clears up a storm, then lying in the sun would clear up everyone's "stormy" red spots. Our town looked like a huge tanning salon.

"Mica, your plan worked. The spots are gone," said the mayor later that day. "I proclaim you Town Scientist!"

Everyone cheered for me! I didn't feel like such a horrible outcast after all. I even went home and had a huge piece of apple pie and a tall glass of ice-cold milk.

Now I have time to reflect on all that's happened. My town doesn't have to worry about space fruit for another century and we owe it all to science.

What's that over there? It's a flower I've never seen before. It looks like it has a ring around it instead of petals. Hmm....

Comprehension Check

Summarize

Complete a Theme Chart with the class. Summarize the story. You can use the chart to help you organize your ideas.

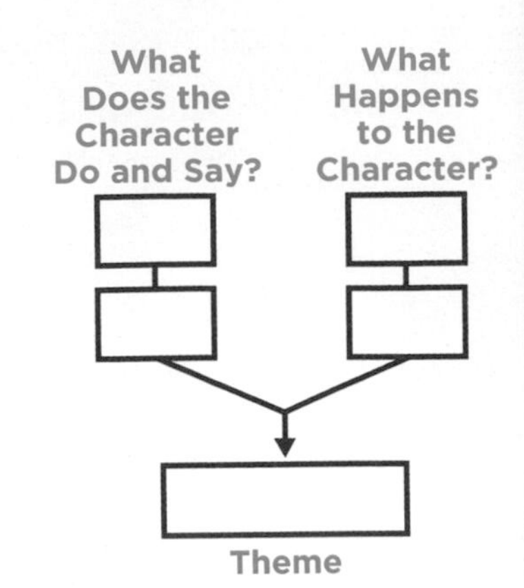

Think and Compare

1. Mica says he feels like an outcast. Find examples in the story that show how he is different from other people. ***(Analyze Theme)***

2. Being different ended up helping Mica in this story. Has being different ever helped you? If so, how? ***(Analyze)***

3. When Mica learns about Jupiter, it helps him help his town. Some people think more money should be spent on the space exploration program. What do you think? ***(Synthesize)***